Digital Kindness Journal

A year of guided reflections
for compassionate social media use

Lauren M. Hug

to be used alone or alongside
Digital Kindness:
Being Human in a Hyper-Connected World
also by Lauren M. Hug

ISBN: 978-1-963046-00-7

Hello! Thank you for choosing this journal to guide you in developing your digital kindness practice.

Inspired by *Digital Kindness: Being Human in a Hyper-Connected World*, this journal can be used as a companion to that book, but is designed as a standalone guided journal experience.

The journal is divided into 3 sections.

The first section contains more than 50 prompts to help you think about your social media use and how it impacts you and others. Most prompts are presented on an unlined 2-page spread so you can answer them by writing, drawing, collaging — whatever works for you!

The middle section provides 30 days (one month) of daily guided digital kindness reflections. It concludes with a template for designing your personal digital kindness plan.

The final section provides 48 weeks of guided digital kindness practice and reflections to solidify habits.

Combined, the sections in this journal guide you through one full year of digital kindness activities and reflections to help you use social media compassionately.

Turn the page to get started!

How do you feel about social media?

What social media networks do you use most?

How do you usually use social media?
Jot down every use you can think of.

What kinds of things do you usually post on social media?

What do you like seeing on social media?

How do you interact on social media with people you also interact with in person?

How do you interact on social media with people you haven't ever met in person?

Map your social media activity for the past week. Use one color to highlight activity you see as positive (things that contributed positively to your life). Use another color to highlight activity you see as negative (things that made you feel anxious, upset, or other unpleasant emotions). **What do you notice?**

Make a plan to increase your positive social media activity next week.

Brainstorm ways to transform negative social media activities from last week into activities that create positive emotions.

List people in your life who have very different backgrounds or views than you.
Note *how* they differ from you.

In digital spaces, how do you usually respond to people who express different views from you?

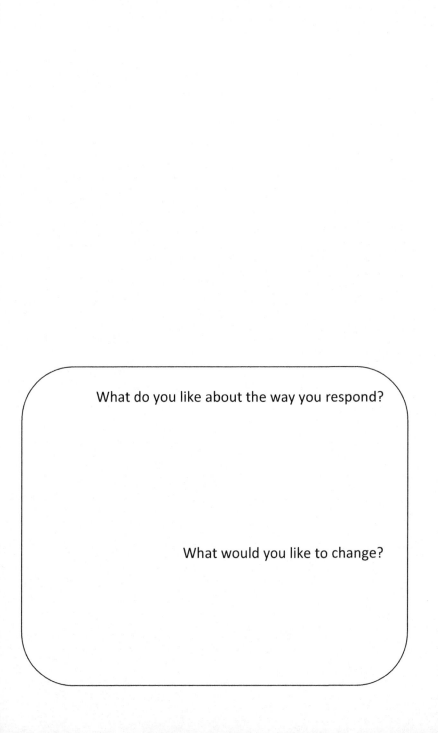

What do you like about the way you respond?

What would you like to change?

Jot down anything you notice as you look over the list.

List the people or accounts you SEE the most on social media.

List the people or accounts you INTERACT WITH most on social media.

Jot down anything you notice as you look over the list.

Has social media opened your eyes to a viewpoint, lifestyle, or experience you hadn't encountered before? How?

Do you believe social media can build bridges and foster positive connections? Why or why not?

I can't believe anyone could ever think

_____

Find at least one person on social media who thinks this.
Spend a week seeing what else they post.

I can't believe anyone could ever think

_____

Find at least one person on social media who thinks this.
Spend a week seeing what else they post.

I can't believe anyone could ever think

_____

Find at least one person on social media who thinks this.
Spend a week seeing what else they post.

Thoughts & Observations

 If you feel like posting is pointless because no one reacts, remember that most people passively consume social media. Everything you post is absolutely being seen by someone. Your voice and experiences matter.

How do you feel when no one likes or reacts to your social media posts?

How do you feel when someone replies to or comments on your post?

How often do you reply to or comment on other people's posts (instead of just clicking a reaction)?

What experiences or knowledge of yours might be helpful, encouraging, or validating to others?

Do you believe replying to someone in a digital space can make a real difference in their life? Why or why not?

Make a list of simple phrases you can use in digital spaces to let people know you see them and value them.

Thoughts &
Observations

For one week, keep a record of every *kind* comment you make in digital spaces. Document the responses you receive. Document how you feel.

Journal about any ways you behave differently in digital spaces than you do in person.

EXCITEMENT	SHAME
JOY	ENVY
SADNESS	JEALOUSY
CURIOSITY	HOPE
ANGER	LONELINESS
FEAR	EMPATHY
LOVE	COMPASSION
SURPRISE	PRIDE
DISGUST	REGRET
HAPPINESS	APPREHENSION
GRIEF	CONFUSION
HUMILITY	FRUSTRATION
RESENTMENT	DISAPPOINTMENT
CONTENTMENT	PEACE
GRATITUDE	CONFUSION
GUILT	AMUSEMENT
CONCERN	BENEVOLENCE

What emotions do you feel when you encounter ideas you disagree with in your social media feeds?
Circle the words that best fit, add others, and write down (or draw) whatever thoughts come to mind.

Write about a time another person's experience changed your perspective on something.

Can people hold truly awful views and still be worthy of compassion? Worthy of friendship? Why or why not?

How do you currently respond to your friends when they post things you strongly disagree with? Why is that the way you choose to respond?

What are some other ways you might consider responding?

In this box, write down names of people you've QUIETLY unfriended or unfollowed. Circle any you regret. Draw a line through ones you're glad you disconnected from.

Have you ever PUBLICLY announced you've "unfriended" someone and/or invited people to "unfriend" you? Why or why not?

List the friends, creators, pages, channels, accounts, podcasts, news sources, etc. that you tend to listen to most.

Rate them on a scale of 1-10.

1 = "We disagree on everything."

10 = "We agree on everything."

What do you notice?

Thoughts &
Observations

Write down some views, perspectives, lifestyles, or experiences you have difficulty understanding.

Name a person you know or a creator you're aware of who "represents" each thing you wrote down.

Spend several weeks listening to these people/creators in digital spaces.

Develop a plan for responding to friends who post things on social media that create negative emotions for you.

What matters most to you?

- ❑ SPEAKING YOUR MIND
- ❑ KEEPING THE PEACE
- ❑ CHANGING MINDS
- ❑ SHARING YOUR EXPERIENCE / PERSPECTIVE
- ❑ LEARNING MORE ABOUT THEIR PERSPECTIVE
- ❑ _____
- ❑ _____
- ❑ _____

Do you want to respond at all?

- ❑ YES   ❑ NO   ❑ DEPENDS

How long do you want to wait to respond?

- ❑ IMMEDIATELY   ❑ BY END OF DAY
- ❑ AN HOUR   ❑ 24 HOURS
- ❑ _____

Write down any other boundaries you'd like to enforce or guidelines you'd like to set for yourself.

Social media is personal *and* public.
Journal about ways you speak differently to one person privately than you do when speaking publicly to a group.

List topics and types of content that bother you in digital spaces.

Circle any that you sometimes post yourself.

Write (or draw) about a time someone
had a reaction to one of your posts that
you didn't expect.

Write (or draw) about a time you saw someone else's post that wasn't intended for you, but it impacted you anyway.

Write (or draw) about a time a friend
posted something that hurt or upset you.
How did you respond?

List everything you think about before you publish a social media post.

Circle anything you *want* to think about before posting.

Cross out anything you *don't want* to think about.

Questions to ask before posting about hot-button issues:

Why am I posting this?

Do I *really* mean this?

Is it possible someone I love or respect will be hurt by this?

Will I be surprised, hurt, or angry if someone decides to argue with me or unfriend me because of this post?

What would you add or subtract?

Brainstorm ways of making your holiday social media posts more considerate of people for whom the holiday may be grief-laden or difficult.

How does the way you're feeling *before* you look at social media impact the way you perceive posts?

How does the way you're feeling impact the way you interact in digital spaces and the types of things you post?

Did you let the authors know their posts were meaningful to you?

Journal about social media posts that moved or impacted you.
What made the posts powerful?

List times in your life where you felt alone and wished you knew of at least one person who had been through a similar experience.

Circle any you might be willing to share about on social media. ♥

Post it! (If you feel up to it.)

Write a draft of a social media post about an experience you've had that could be helpful to others going through something similar.

How do you distinguish between posts that share difficult experiences for the sake of helping others and those primarily designed to get attention and maximize engagement?

Find three posts by different people about the same difficult subject. Journal about the feelings each post evokes in you.

Lives are intertwined.
Write about how you want to handle sharing in digital spaces about difficult things in your life that involve others.

EXCITEMENT	SHAME
JOY	ENVY
SADNESS	JEALOUSY
CURIOSITY	HOPE
ANGER	LONELINESS
FEAR	EMPATHY
LOVE	COMPASSION
SURPRISE	PRIDE
DISGUST	REGRET
HAPPINESS	APPREHENSION
GRIEF	CONFUSION
HUMILITY	FRUSTRATION
RESENTMENT	DISAPPOINTMENT
CONTENTMENT	PEACE
GRATITUDE	CONFUSION
GUILT	AMUSEMENT
CONCERN	BENEVOLENCE

What emotions do you experience when navigating digital spaces?
Circle the words that best fit, add others and write down (or draw) whatever thoughts come to mind.

List topics, types of content, people, or accounts that affect you negatively in digital spaces.

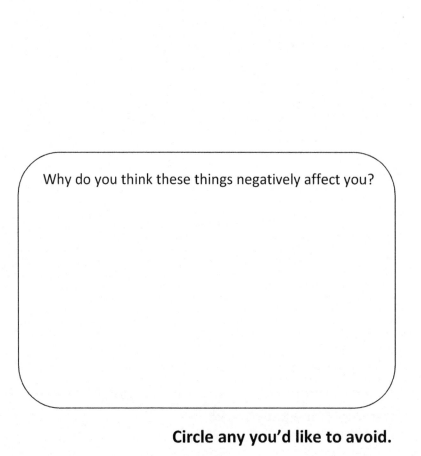

Why do you think these things negatively affect you?

Circle any you'd like to avoid.

Find and follow at least 10 accounts posting the things you want to see!

List topics, types of content, people, and accounts you'd like to see more of in digital spaces.

Track your social media activity for 1 day.

Take a look at:

- How much time you spend in digital spaces
- Which networks you're using
- What content impacts you
- Which people impact you
- What you choose to visibly respond to
- How you choose to respond
- Anything else you notice

Note anything that surprises you.

Note anything you'd like to do differently.

Write about a time you regretted something you posted (or the way you interacted) on social media AND what you learned from the experience.

Look for a post that makes you angry. Take a deep breath, and respond in kindness.

Write about how you feel AND any reactions to your response.

How can your kindness in digital spaces change the world (or at least one small corner of it)?

How do you want to show kindness in digital spaces?

Congratulations! You've completed the first section of this journal!

The next section has space for you to track and reflect on your social media experiences every day for one month.

After that, you'll find an outline for developing **your** personal digital kindness plan based on what you've discovered from your month of reflections and from completing the prompts on the previous pages.

30 DAYS OF
DIGITAL KINDNESS
REFLECTIONS

How I felt in digital spaces today

What I posted today

Positive content I saw (and my response)

Negative content I saw (and my response)

TODAY I LEARNED

A KIND THING I DID ONLINE

OTHER REFLECTIONS

TIME SPENT ON SOCIAL MEDIA

Time on _____: _____
(social media network)

Time on_____: _____
(social media network)

Time on _____: _____
(social media network)

Time on_____: _____
(social media network)

How I felt in digital spaces today

What I posted today

Positive content I saw (and my response)

Negative content I saw (and my response)

DAY 2

TODAY I LEARNED

A KIND THING I DID ONLINE

OTHER REFLECTIONS

TIME SPENT ON SOCIAL MEDIA

Time on _____: _____   Time on_____: _____
(social media network)   *(social media network)*

Time on _____: _____   Time on_____: _____
(social media network)   *(social media network)*

HOW I FELT IN DIGITAL SPACES TODAY

WHAT I POSTED TODAY

POSITIVE CONTENT I SAW (AND MY RESPONSE)

NEGATIVE CONTENT I SAW (AND MY RESPONSE)

DAY 3

<u>TODAY I LEARNED</u>

<u>A KIND THING I DID ONLINE</u>

<u>OTHER REFLECTIONS</u>

<u>TIME SPENT ON SOCIAL MEDIA</u>

Time on _____: _____   Time on_____: _____
      (social media network)   *(social media network)*

Time on _____: _____   Time on_____: _____
      (social media network)   *(social media network)*

How I felt in digital spaces today

What I posted today

Positive content I saw (and my response)

Negative content I saw (and my response)

TODAY I LEARNED

A KIND THING I DID ONLINE

OTHER REFLECTIONS

TIME SPENT ON SOCIAL MEDIA

Time on _____ : _____   Time on_____ : _____
(social media network)   *(social media network)*

Time on _____ : _____   Time on_____ : _____
(social media network)   *(social media network)*

HOW I FELT IN DIGITAL SPACES TODAY

WHAT I POSTED TODAY

POSITIVE CONTENT I SAW (AND MY RESPONSE)

NEGATIVE CONTENT I SAW (AND MY RESPONSE)

DAY 5

<u>TODAY</u> I LEARNED

<u>A</u> KIND THING I DID ONLINE

<u>O</u>THER REFLECTIONS

<u>TIME</u> SPENT ON SOCIAL MEDIA

Time on _____: _____   Time on_____: _____
      (social media network)   *(social media network)*

Time on _____: _____   Time on_____: _____
      (social media network)   *(social media network)*

HOW I FELT IN DIGITAL SPACES TODAY

WHAT I POSTED TODAY

POSITIVE CONTENT I SAW (AND MY RESPONSE)

NEGATIVE CONTENT I SAW (AND MY RESPONSE)

TODAY I LEARNED

A KIND THING I DID ONLINE

OTHER REFLECTIONS

TIME SPENT ON SOCIAL MEDIA

Time on _____ : _____
(social media network)

Time on_____ : _____
(social media network)

Time on _____ : _____
(social media network)

Time on_____ : _____
(social media network)

HOW I FELT IN DIGITAL SPACES TODAY

WHAT I POSTED TODAY

POSITIVE CONTENT I SAW (AND MY RESPONSE)

NEGATIVE CONTENT I SAW (AND MY RESPONSE)

DAY 7

<u>TODAY I LEARNED</u>

<u>A KIND THING I DID ONLINE</u>

<u>OTHER REFLECTIONS</u>

<u>TIME SPENT ON SOCIAL MEDIA</u>

Time on _____: _____   Time on_____: _____
(social media network)   *(social media network)*

Time on _____: _____   Time on_____: _____
(social media network)   *(social media network)*

HOW I FELT IN DIGITAL SPACES TODAY

WHAT I POSTED TODAY

POSITIVE CONTENT I SAW (AND MY RESPONSE)

NEGATIVE CONTENT I SAW (AND MY RESPONSE)

DAY 8

<u>TODAY I LEARNED</u>

<u>A KIND THING I DID ONLINE</u>

<u>OTHER REFLECTIONS</u>

<u>TIME SPENT ON SOCIAL MEDIA</u>

Time on _____: _____   Time on_____: _____
       (social media network)   *(social media network)*

Time on _____: _____   Time on_____: _____
       (social media network)   *(social media network)*

How I felt in digital spaces today

What I posted today

Positive content I saw (and my response)

Negative content I saw (and my response)

DAY 9

<u>TODAY I LEARNED</u>

<u>A KIND THING I DID ONLINE</u>

<u>OTHER REFLECTIONS</u>

<u>TIME SPENT ON SOCIAL MEDIA</u>

Time on _____: _____   Time on_____: _____
      (social media network)   *(social media network)*

Time on _____: _____   Time on_____: _____
      (social media network)   *(social media network)*

How I felt in digital spaces today

What I posted today

Positive content I saw (and my response)

Negative content I saw (and my response)

DAY 10

<u>TODAY I LEARNED</u>

<u>A KIND THING I DID ONLINE</u>

<u>OTHER REFLECTIONS</u>

<u>TIME SPENT ON SOCIAL MEDIA</u>

Time on _____: _____
(social media network)

Time on_____: _____
(social media network)

Time on _____: _____
(social media network)

Time on_____: _____
(social media network)

How I felt in digital spaces today

What I posted today

Positive content I saw (and my response)

Negative content I saw (and my response)

DAY 11

TODAY I LEARNED

A KIND THING I DID ONLINE

OTHER REFLECTIONS

TIME SPENT ON SOCIAL MEDIA

Time on _____: _____   Time on_____: _____
(social media network)   *(social media network)*

Time on _____: _____   Time on_____: _____
(social media network)   *(social media network)*

HOW I FELT IN DIGITAL SPACES TODAY

WHAT I POSTED TODAY

POSITIVE CONTENT I SAW (AND MY RESPONSE)

NEGATIVE CONTENT I SAW (AND MY RESPONSE)

DAY 12

TODAY I LEARNED

A KIND THING I DID ONLINE

OTHER REFLECTIONS

TIME SPENT ON SOCIAL MEDIA

Time on _____ : _____   Time on_____ : _____
      (social media network)   *(social media network)*

Time on _____ : _____   Time on_____ : _____
      (social media network)   *(social media network)*

HOW I FELT IN DIGITAL SPACES TODAY

WHAT I POSTED TODAY

POSITIVE CONTENT I SAW (AND MY RESPONSE)

NEGATIVE CONTENT I SAW (AND MY RESPONSE)

TODAY I LEARNED

A KIND THING I DID ONLINE

OTHER REFLECTIONS

TIME SPENT ON SOCIAL MEDIA

Time on _____: _____
(social media network)

Time on_____: _____
(social media network)

Time on _____: _____
(social media network)

Time on_____: _____
(social media network)

How I felt in digital spaces today

What I posted today

Positive content I saw (and my response)

Negative content I saw (and my response)

TODAY I LEARNED

A KIND THING I DID ONLINE

OTHER REFLECTIONS

TIME SPENT ON SOCIAL MEDIA

Time on _____: _____
(social media network)

Time on_____: _____
(social media network)

Time on _____: _____
(social media network)

Time on_____: _____
(social media network)

HOW I FELT IN DIGITAL SPACES TODAY

WHAT I POSTED TODAY

POSITIVE CONTENT I SAW (AND MY RESPONSE)

NEGATIVE CONTENT I SAW (AND MY RESPONSE)

TODAY I LEARNED

A KIND THING I DID ONLINE

OTHER REFLECTIONS

TIME SPENT ON SOCIAL MEDIA

Time on _____: _____
(social media network)

Time on_____: _____
(social media network)

Time on _____: _____
(social media network)

Time on_____: _____
(social media network)

How I felt in digital spaces today

What I posted today

Positive content I saw (and my response)

Negative content I saw (and my response)

TODAY I LEARNED

A KIND THING I DID ONLINE

OTHER REFLECTIONS

TIME SPENT ON SOCIAL MEDIA

Time on _____: _____   Time on_____: _____
(social media network)   *(social media network)*

Time on _____: _____   Time on_____: _____
(social media network)   *(social media network)*

How I felt in digital spaces today

What I posted today

Positive content I saw (and my response)

Negative content I saw (and my response)

DAY 17

<u>TODAY I LEARNED</u>

<u>A KIND THING I DID ONLINE</u>

<u>OTHER REFLECTIONS</u>

<u>TIME SPENT ON SOCIAL MEDIA</u>

Time on _____: _____   Time on_____: _____
        (social media network)   *(social media network)*

Time on _____: _____   Time on_____: _____
        (social media network)   *(social media network)*

How I felt in digital spaces today

What I posted today

Positive content I saw (and my response)

Negative content I saw (and my response)

DAY 18

<u>TODAY I LEARNED</u>

<u>A KIND THING I DID ONLINE</u>

<u>OTHER REFLECTIONS</u>

<u>TIME SPENT ON SOCIAL MEDIA</u>

Time on _____: _____
(social media network)

Time on_____: _____
(social media network)

Time on _____: _____
(social media network)

Time on_____: _____
(social media network)

How I felt in digital spaces today

What I posted today

Positive content I saw (and my response)

Negative content I saw (and my response)

DAY 19

<u>TODAY I LEARNED</u>

<u>A KIND THING I DID ONLINE</u>

<u>OTHER REFLECTIONS</u>

<u>TIME SPENT ON SOCIAL MEDIA</u>

Time on _____ : _____   Time on _____ : _____
(social media network)   *(social media network)*

Time on _____ : _____   Time on _____ : _____
(social media network)   *(social media network)*

How I felt in digital spaces today

What I posted today

Positive content I saw (and my response)

Negative content I saw (and my response)

TODAY I LEARNED

A KIND THING I DID ONLINE

OTHER REFLECTIONS

TIME SPENT ON SOCIAL MEDIA

Time on _____: _____   Time on_____: _____
(social media network)   *(social media network)*

Time on _____: _____   Time on_____: _____
(social media network)   *(social media network)*

HOW I FELT IN DIGITAL SPACES TODAY

WHAT I POSTED TODAY

POSITIVE CONTENT I SAW (AND MY RESPONSE)

NEGATIVE CONTENT I SAW (AND MY RESPONSE)

DAY 21

<u>TODAY I LEARNED</u>

<u>A KIND THING I DID ONLINE</u>

<u>OTHER REFLECTIONS</u>

<u>TIME SPENT ON SOCIAL MEDIA</u>

Time on _____: _____   Time on_____: _____
     (social media network)   *(social media network)*

Time on _____: _____   Time on_____: _____
     (social media network)   *(social media network)*

HOW I FELT IN DIGITAL SPACES TODAY

WHAT I POSTED TODAY

POSITIVE CONTENT I SAW (AND MY RESPONSE)

NEGATIVE CONTENT I SAW (AND MY RESPONSE)

TODAY I LEARNED

A KIND THING I DID ONLINE

OTHER REFLECTIONS

TIME SPENT ON SOCIAL MEDIA

Time on _____: _____   Time on_____: _____
        (social media network)   *(social media network)*

Time on _____: _____   Time on_____: _____
        (social media network)   *(social media network)*

How I felt in digital spaces today

What I posted today

Positive content I saw (and my response)

Negative content I saw (and my response)

DAY 23

<u>TODAY I LEARNED</u>

<u>A KIND THING I DID ONLINE</u>

<u>OTHER REFLECTIONS</u>

<u>TIME SPENT ON SOCIAL MEDIA</u>

Time on _____: _____
(social media network)

TIme on_____: _____
(social media network)

Time on _____: _____
(social media network)

Time on_____: _____
(social media network)

HOW I FELT IN DIGITAL SPACES TODAY

WHAT I POSTED TODAY

POSITIVE CONTENT I SAW (AND MY RESPONSE)

NEGATIVE CONTENT I SAW (AND MY RESPONSE)

DAY 24

<u>TODAY I LEARNED</u>

<u>A KIND THING I DID ONLINE</u>

<u>OTHER REFLECTIONS</u>

<u>TIME SPENT ON SOCIAL MEDIA</u>

Time on _____ : _____   Time on_____ : _____
   (social media network)   *(social media network)*

Time on _____ : _____   Time on_____ : _____
   (social media network)   *(social media network)*

How I felt in digital spaces today

What I posted today

Positive content I saw (and my response)

Negative content I saw (and my response)

DAY 25

<u>TODAY I LEARNED</u>

<u>A KIND THING I DID ONLINE</u>

<u>OTHER REFLECTIONS</u>

<u>TIME SPENT ON SOCIAL MEDIA</u>

Time on _____: _____   Time on_____: _____
        (social media network)   *(social media network)*

Time on _____: _____   Time on_____: _____
        (social media network)   *(social media network)*

How I felt in digital spaces today

What I posted today

Positive content I saw (and my response)

Negative content I saw (and my response)

TODAY I LEARNED

A KIND THING I DID ONLINE

OTHER REFLECTIONS

TIME SPENT ON SOCIAL MEDIA

Time on _____: _____   Time on_____: _____
       (social media network)   *(social media network)*

Time on _____: _____   Time on_____: _____
       (social media network)   *(social media network)*

HOW I FELT IN DIGITAL SPACES TODAY

WHAT I POSTED TODAY

POSITIVE CONTENT I SAW (AND MY RESPONSE)

NEGATIVE CONTENT I SAW (AND MY RESPONSE)

DAY 27

TODAY I LEARNED

A KIND THING I DID ONLINE

OTHER REFLECTIONS

TIME SPENT ON SOCIAL MEDIA

Time on _____: _____
(social media network)

Time on_____: _____
(social media network)

Time on _____: _____
(social media network)

Time on_____: _____
(social media network)

How I felt in digital spaces today

What I posted today

Positive content I saw (and my response)

Negative content I saw (and my response)

DAY 28

TODAY I LEARNED

A KIND THING I DID ONLINE

OTHER REFLECTIONS

TIME SPENT ON SOCIAL MEDIA

Time on _____ : _____
(social media network)

Time on_____ : _____
(social media network)

Time on _____ : _____
(social media network)

Time on_____ : _____
(social media network)

How I felt in digital spaces today

What I posted today

Positive content I saw (and my response)

Negative content I saw (and my response)

TODAY I LEARNED

A KIND THING I DID ONLINE

OTHER REFLECTIONS

TIME SPENT ON SOCIAL MEDIA

Time on _____: _____   Time on_____: _____
        (social media network)   *(social media network)*

Time on _____: _____   Time on_____: _____
        (social media network)   *(social media network)*

How I felt in digital spaces today

What I posted today

Positive content I saw (and my response)

Negative content I saw (and my response)

TODAY I LEARNED

A KIND THING I DID ONLINE

OTHER REFLECTIONS

TIME SPENT ON SOCIAL MEDIA

Time on _____ : _____   Time on _____ : _____
       (social media network)   *(social media network)*

Time on _____ : _____   Time on _____ : _____
       (social media network)   *(social media network)*

You did it! You completed 30 days of digital kindness reflections!
Look through your reflections and responses to the prompts earlier in this journal. What stands out to you most?

The next few pages will guide you in creating **your** digital kindness plan.

MY DIGITAL KINDNESS PLAN

Content, people, and accounts I want to see:

Content, people, and accounts I don't want to see:

Things I want to learn more about:

Things I want to share about on social media:

How I'll share my experiences involving other people:

Ways I'll show kindness:

Things I want to think about before posting:

How I'll respond to posts that create negative feelings:

My criteria for unfriending/unfollowing:

My criteria for deciding I need a social media break:

Daily time limit for **all** social media: _____

Daily time limit for _____: _____
(social media network)

Daily time limit for _____: _____
(social media network)

Daily time limit for _____: _____
(social media network)

Daily time limit for _____: _____
(social media network)

Anything else I want to include in my plan:

Use the next 2 pages, if you need more space …

more space for creating
My Digital Kindness Plan ...

Congratulations on creating your personal digital kindness plan!

The final section of this journal has space for you to document 48 weeks of your digital kindness practice and reflections.

48 WEEKS OF
DIGITAL KINDNESS
PRACTICE & REFLECTIONS

HOW I FELT IN DIGITAL SPACES THIS WEEK

THINGS I POSTED THIS WEEK

POSITIVE CONTENT I SAW (AND MY RESPONSE)

NEGATIVE CONTENT I SAW (AND MY RESPONSE)

WEEK 1

THINGS I LEARNED THIS WEEK

KIND THINGS I DID ONLINE

OTHER REFLECTIONS

AVERAGE TIME SPENT DAILY ON SOCIAL MEDIA THIS WEEK

Time on _____ : _____   Time on_____ : _____
      (social media network)   *(social media network)*

Time on _____ : _____   Time on_____ : _____
      (social media network)   *(social media network)*

HOW I FELT IN DIGITAL SPACES THIS WEEK

THINGS I POSTED THIS WEEK

POSITIVE CONTENT I SAW (AND MY RESPONSE)

NEGATIVE CONTENT I SAW (AND MY RESPONSE)

WEEK 2

THINGS I LEARNED THIS WEEK

KIND THINGS I DID ONLINE

OTHER REFLECTIONS

AVERAGE TIME SPENT DAILY ON SOCIAL MEDIA THIS WEEK

Time on _____: _____   Time on _____: _____
(social media network)   *(social media network)*

Time on _____: _____   Time on _____: _____
(social media network)   *(social media network)*

HOW I FELT IN DIGITAL SPACES THIS WEEK

THINGS I POSTED THIS WEEK

POSITIVE CONTENT I SAW (AND MY RESPONSE)

NEGATIVE CONTENT I SAW (AND MY RESPONSE)

WEEK 3

THINGS I LEARNED THIS WEEK

KIND THINGS I DID ONLINE

OTHER REFLECTIONS

AVERAGE TIME SPENT DAILY ON SOCIAL MEDIA THIS WEEK

Time on _____ : _____   Time on _____ : _____
(social media network)   *(social media network)*

Time on _____ : _____   Time on _____ : _____
(social media network)   *(social media network)*

HOW I FELT IN DIGITAL SPACES THIS WEEK

THINGS I POSTED THIS WEEK

POSITIVE CONTENT I SAW (AND MY RESPONSE)

NEGATIVE CONTENT I SAW (AND MY RESPONSE)

WEEK 4

THINGS I LEARNED THIS WEEK

KIND THINGS I DID ONLINE

OTHER REFLECTIONS

AVERAGE TIME SPENT DAILY ON SOCIAL MEDIA THIS WEEK

Time on _____: _____
(social media network)

Time on_____: _____
(social media network)

Time on _____: _____
(social media network)

Time on_____: _____
(social media network)

Congratulations! You've completed 1 month of reflections following your digital kindness plan!

What are you noticing about yourself and kindness in digital spaces?

How I felt in digital spaces this week

Things I posted this week

Positive content I saw (and my response)

Negative content I saw (and my response)

WEEK 5

THINGS I LEARNED THIS WEEK

KIND THINGS I DID ONLINE

OTHER REFLECTIONS

AVERAGE TIME SPENT DAILY ON SOCIAL MEDIA THIS WEEK

Time on _____ : _____   Time on _____ : _____
        (social media network)   *(social media network)*

Time on _____ : _____   Time on _____ : _____
        (social media network)   *(social media network)*

How I felt in digital spaces this week

Things I posted this week

Positive content I saw (and my response)

Negative content I saw (and my response)

THINGS I LEARNED THIS WEEK

KIND THINGS I DID ONLINE

OTHER REFLECTIONS

AVERAGE TIME SPENT DAILY ON SOCIAL MEDIA THIS WEEK

Time on _____: _____   Time on_____: _____
(social media network)   *(social media network)*

Time on _____: _____   Time on_____: _____
(social media network)   *(social media network)*

How I felt in digital spaces this week

Things I posted this week

Positive content I saw (and my response)

Negative content I saw (and my response)

WEEK 7

<u>T</u>HINGS I LEARNED THIS WEEK

<u>K</u>IND THINGS I DID ONLINE

<u>O</u>THER REFLECTIONS

<u>A</u>VERAGE TIME SPENT DAILY ON SOCIAL MEDIA THIS WEEK

Time on _____: _____
(social media network)

Time on _____: _____
(social media network)

Time on _____: _____
(social media network)

Time on _____: _____
(social media network)

How I felt in digital spaces this week

Things I posted this week

Positive content I saw (and my response)

Negative content I saw (and my response)

<u>THINGS I LEARNED THIS WEEK</u>

<u>KIND THINGS I DID ONLINE</u>

<u>OTHER REFLECTIONS</u>

<u>AVERAGE TIME SPENT DAILY ON SOCIAL MEDIA THIS WEEK</u>

Time on _____: _____
(social media network)

Time on_____: _____
(social media network)

Time on _____: _____
(social media network)

Time on_____: _____
(social media network)

Congratulations! You've completed 2 months of reflections following your digital kindness plan!

What are you noticing about yourself and kindness in digital spaces?

HOW I FELT IN DIGITAL SPACES THIS WEEK

THINGS I POSTED THIS WEEK

POSITIVE CONTENT I SAW (AND MY RESPONSE)

NEGATIVE CONTENT I SAW (AND MY RESPONSE)

WEEK 9

THINGS I LEARNED THIS WEEK

KIND THINGS I DID ONLINE

OTHER REFLECTIONS

AVERAGE TIME SPENT DAILY ON SOCIAL MEDIA THIS WEEK

Time on _____: _____
(social media network)

Time on_____: _____
(social media network)

Time on _____: _____
(social media network)

Time on_____: _____
(social media network)

How I felt in digital spaces this week

Things I posted this week

Positive content I saw (and my response)

Negative content I saw (and my response)

THINGS I LEARNED THIS WEEK

KIND THINGS I DID ONLINE

OTHER REFLECTIONS

AVERAGE TIME SPENT DAILY ON SOCIAL MEDIA THIS WEEK

Time on _____: _____   Time on_____: _____
    (social media network)   *(social media network)*

Time on _____: _____   Time on_____: _____
    (social media network)   *(social media network)*

How I felt in digital spaces this week

Things I posted this week

Positive content I saw (and my response)

Negative content I saw (and my response)

THINGS I LEARNED THIS WEEK

KIND THINGS I DID ONLINE

OTHER REFLECTIONS

AVERAGE TIME SPENT DAILY ON SOCIAL MEDIA THIS WEEK

Time on _____: _____
(social media network)

Time on_____: _____
(social media network)

Time on _____: _____
(social media network)

Time on_____: _____
(social media network)

HOW I FELT IN DIGITAL SPACES THIS WEEK

THINGS I POSTED THIS WEEK

POSITIVE CONTENT I SAW (AND MY RESPONSE)

NEGATIVE CONTENT I SAW (AND MY RESPONSE)

WEEK 12

THINGS I LEARNED THIS WEEK

KIND THINGS I DID ONLINE

OTHER REFLECTIONS

AVERAGE TIME SPENT DAILY ON SOCIAL MEDIA THIS WEEK

Time on _____: _____
(social media network)

Time on _____: _____
(social media network)

Time on _____: _____
(social media network)

Time on _____: _____
(social media network)

Congratulations! You've completed 3 months of reflections following your digital kindness plan!
What are you noticing about yourself and kindness in digital spaces?

How I felt in digital spaces this week

Things I posted this week

Positive content I saw (and my response)

Negative content I saw (and my response)

THINGS I LEARNED THIS WEEK

KIND THINGS I DID ONLINE

OTHER REFLECTIONS

AVERAGE TIME SPENT DAILY ON SOCIAL MEDIA THIS WEEK

Time on _____: _____
(social media network)

Time on _____: _____
(social media network)

Time on _____: _____
(social media network)

Time on _____: _____
(social media network)

HOW I FELT IN DIGITAL SPACES THIS WEEK

THINGS I POSTED THIS WEEK

POSITIVE CONTENT I SAW (AND MY RESPONSE)

NEGATIVE CONTENT I SAW (AND MY RESPONSE)

WEEK 14

THINGS I LEARNED THIS WEEK

KIND THINGS I DID ONLINE

OTHER REFLECTIONS

AVERAGE TIME SPENT DAILY ON SOCIAL MEDIA THIS WEEK

Time on _____: _____   Time on_____: _____
(social media network)   *(social media network)*

Time on _____: _____   Time on_____: _____
(social media network)   *(social media network)*

How I felt in digital spaces this week

Things I posted this week

Positive content I saw (and my response)

Negative content I saw (and my response)

THINGS I LEARNED THIS WEEK

KIND THINGS I DID ONLINE

OTHER REFLECTIONS

AVERAGE TIME SPENT DAILY ON SOCIAL MEDIA THIS WEEK

Time on _____: _____
(social media network)

Time on_____ : _____
(social media network)

Time on _____: _____
(social media network)

Time on_____: _____
(social media network)

How I felt in digital spaces this week

Things I posted this week

Positive content I saw (and my response)

Negative content I saw (and my response)

THINGS I LEARNED THIS WEEK

KIND THINGS I DID ONLINE

OTHER REFLECTIONS

AVERAGE TIME SPENT DAILY ON SOCIAL MEDIA THIS WEEK

Time on _____: _____   Time on_____: _____
(social media network)   _(social media network)_

Time on _____: _____   Time on_____: _____
(social media network)   _(social media network)_

Congratulations! You've completed 4 months of reflections following your digital kindness plan!

What are you noticing about yourself and kindness in digital spaces?

How I felt in digital spaces this week

Things I posted this week

Positive content I saw (and my response)

Negative content I saw (and my response)

THINGS I LEARNED THIS WEEK

KIND THINGS I DID ONLINE

OTHER REFLECTIONS

AVERAGE TIME SPENT DAILY ON SOCIAL MEDIA THIS WEEK

Time on _____: _____   Time on_____: _____
(social media network)   *(social media network)*

Time on _____: _____   Time on_____: _____
(social media network)   *(social media network)*

How I felt in digital spaces this week

Things I posted this week

Positive content I saw (and my response)

Negative content I saw (and my response)

THINGS I LEARNED THIS WEEK

KIND THINGS I DID ONLINE

OTHER REFLECTIONS

AVERAGE TIME SPENT DAILY ON SOCIAL MEDIA THIS WEEK

Time on _____ : _____
      (social media network)

Time on _____ : _____
      (social media network)

Time on _____ : _____
      (social media network)

Time on _____ : _____
      (social media network)

How I felt in digital spaces this week

Things I posted this week

Positive content I saw (and my response)

Negative content I saw (and my response)

THINGS I LEARNED THIS WEEK

KIND THINGS I DID ONLINE

OTHER REFLECTIONS

AVERAGE TIME SPENT DAILY ON SOCIAL MEDIA THIS WEEK

Time on _____: _____
(social media network)

Time on_____: _____
(social media network)

Time on _____: _____
(social media network)

Time on_____: _____
(social media network)

HOW I FELT IN DIGITAL SPACES THIS WEEK

THINGS I POSTED THIS WEEK

POSITIVE CONTENT I SAW (AND MY RESPONSE)

NEGATIVE CONTENT I SAW (AND MY RESPONSE)

THINGS I LEARNED THIS WEEK

KIND THINGS I DID ONLINE

OTHER REFLECTIONS

AVERAGE TIME SPENT DAILY ON SOCIAL MEDIA THIS WEEK

Time on _____: _____
(social media network)

Time on_____: _____
(social media network)

Time on _____: _____
(social media network)

Time on_____: _____
(social media network)

Congratulations! You've completed 5 months of digital kindness reflections! What are you noticing about yourself and kindness in digital spaces?

HOW I FELT IN DIGITAL SPACES THIS WEEK

THINGS I POSTED THIS WEEK

POSITIVE CONTENT I SAW (AND MY RESPONSE)

NEGATIVE CONTENT I SAW (AND MY RESPONSE)

THINGS I LEARNED THIS WEEK

KIND THINGS I DID ONLINE

OTHER REFLECTIONS

AVERAGE TIME SPENT DAILY ON SOCIAL MEDIA THIS WEEK

Time on _____: _____
(social media network)

Time on_____: _____
(social media network)

Time on _____: _____
(social media network)

Time on_____: _____
(social media network)

HOW I FELT IN DIGITAL SPACES THIS WEEK

THINGS I POSTED THIS WEEK

POSITIVE CONTENT I SAW (AND MY RESPONSE)

NEGATIVE CONTENT I SAW (AND MY RESPONSE)

WEEK 22

THINGS I LEARNED THIS WEEK

KIND THINGS I DID ONLINE

OTHER REFLECTIONS

AVERAGE TIME SPENT DAILY ON SOCIAL MEDIA THIS WEEK

Time on _____: _____
(social media network)

Time on_____: _____
(social media network)

Time on _____: _____
(social media network)

Time on_____: _____
(social media network)

How I felt in digital spaces this week

Things I posted this week

Positive content I saw (and my response)

Negative content I saw (and my response)

WEEK 23

THINGS I LEARNED THIS WEEK

KIND THINGS I DID ONLINE

OTHER REFLECTIONS

AVERAGE TIME SPENT DAILY ON SOCIAL MEDIA THIS WEEK

Time on _____: _____
(social media network)

Time on _____: _____
(social media network)

Time on _____: _____
(social media network)

Time on _____: _____
(social media network)

HOW I FELT IN DIGITAL SPACES THIS WEEK

THINGS I POSTED THIS WEEK

POSITIVE CONTENT I SAW (AND MY RESPONSE)

NEGATIVE CONTENT I SAW (AND MY RESPONSE)

THINGS I LEARNED THIS WEEK

KIND THINGS I DID ONLINE

OTHER REFLECTIONS

AVERAGE TIME SPENT DAILY ON SOCIAL MEDIA THIS WEEK

Time on _____: _____
(social media network)

Time on_____: _____
(social media network)

Time on _____: _____
(social media network)

Time on_____: _____
(social media network)

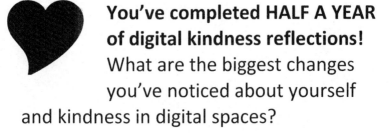

You've completed HALF A YEAR of digital kindness reflections! What are the biggest changes you've noticed about yourself and kindness in digital spaces?

HOW I FELT IN DIGITAL SPACES THIS WEEK

THINGS I POSTED THIS WEEK

POSITIVE CONTENT I SAW (AND MY RESPONSE)

NEGATIVE CONTENT I SAW (AND MY RESPONSE)

THINGS I LEARNED THIS WEEK

KIND THINGS I DID ONLINE

OTHER REFLECTIONS

AVERAGE TIME SPENT DAILY ON SOCIAL MEDIA THIS WEEK

Time on _____: _____
(social media network)

Time on _____: _____
(social media network)

Time on _____: _____
(social media network)

Time on_____: _____
(social media network)

How I felt in digital spaces this week

Things I posted this week

Positive content I saw (and my response)

Negative content I saw (and my response)

THINGS I LEARNED THIS WEEK

KIND THINGS I DID ONLINE

OTHER REFLECTIONS

AVERAGE TIME SPENT DAILY ON SOCIAL MEDIA THIS WEEK

Time on _____: _____   Time on_____: _____
    (social media network)   *(social media network)*

Time on _____: _____   Time on_____: _____
    (social media network)   *(social media network)*

HOW I FELT IN DIGITAL SPACES THIS WEEK

THINGS I POSTED THIS WEEK

POSITIVE CONTENT I SAW (AND MY RESPONSE)

NEGATIVE CONTENT I SAW (AND MY RESPONSE)

THINGS I LEARNED THIS WEEK

KIND THINGS I DID ONLINE

OTHER REFLECTIONS

AVERAGE TIME SPENT DAILY ON SOCIAL MEDIA THIS WEEK

Time on _____: _____   Time on_____: _____
(social media network)   *(social media network)*

Time on _____: _____   Time on_____: _____
(social media network)   *(social media network)*

HOW I FELT IN DIGITAL SPACES THIS WEEK

THINGS I POSTED THIS WEEK

POSITIVE CONTENT I SAW (AND MY RESPONSE)

NEGATIVE CONTENT I SAW (AND MY RESPONSE)

THINGS I LEARNED THIS WEEK

KIND THINGS I DID ONLINE

OTHER REFLECTIONS

AVERAGE TIME SPENT DAILY ON SOCIAL MEDIA THIS WEEK

Time on _____: _____   Time on_____: _____
     (social media network)   *(social media network)*

Time on _____: _____   Time on_____: _____
     (social media network)   *(social media network)*

HOW I FELT IN DIGITAL SPACES THIS WEEK

THINGS I POSTED THIS WEEK

POSITIVE CONTENT I SAW (AND MY RESPONSE)

NEGATIVE CONTENT I SAW (AND MY RESPONSE)

THINGS I LEARNED THIS WEEK

KIND THINGS I DID ONLINE

OTHER REFLECTIONS

AVERAGE TIME SPENT DAILY ON SOCIAL MEDIA THIS WEEK

Time on _____: _____   Time on_____: _____
            (social media network)   *(social media network)*

Time on _____: _____   Time on_____: _____
            (social media network)   *(social media network)*

How I felt in digital spaces this week

Things I posted this week

Positive content I saw (and my response)

Negative content I saw (and my response)

THINGS I LEARNED THIS WEEK

KIND THINGS I DID ONLINE

OTHER REFLECTIONS

AVERAGE TIME SPENT DAILY ON SOCIAL MEDIA THIS WEEK

Time on _____: _____
(social media network)

Time on _____: _____
(social media network)

Time on _____: _____
(social media network)

Time on _____: _____
(social media network)

HOW I FELT IN DIGITAL SPACES THIS WEEK

THINGS I POSTED THIS WEEK

POSITIVE CONTENT I SAW (AND MY RESPONSE)

NEGATIVE CONTENT I SAW (AND MY RESPONSE)

WEEK 31

THINGS I LEARNED THIS WEEK

KIND THINGS I DID ONLINE

OTHER REFLECTIONS

AVERAGE TIME SPENT DAILY ON SOCIAL MEDIA THIS WEEK

Time on _____: _____
(social media network)

Time on _____: _____
(social media network)

Time on _____: _____
(social media network)

Time on _____: _____
(social media network)

HOW I FELT IN DIGITAL SPACES THIS WEEK

THINGS I POSTED THIS WEEK

POSITIVE CONTENT I SAW (AND MY RESPONSE)

NEGATIVE CONTENT I SAW (AND MY RESPONSE)

THINGS I LEARNED THIS WEEK

KIND THINGS I DID ONLINE

OTHER REFLECTIONS

AVERAGE TIME SPENT DAILY ON SOCIAL MEDIA THIS WEEK

Time on _____: _____   Time on _____: _____
(social media network)   *(social media network)*

Time on _____: _____   Time on _____: _____
(social media network)   *(social media network)*

HOW I FELT IN DIGITAL SPACES THIS WEEK

THINGS I POSTED THIS WEEK

POSITIVE CONTENT I SAW (AND MY RESPONSE)

NEGATIVE CONTENT I SAW (AND MY RESPONSE)

THINGS I LEARNED THIS WEEK

KIND THINGS I DID ONLINE

OTHER REFLECTIONS

AVERAGE TIME SPENT DAILY ON SOCIAL MEDIA THIS WEEK

Time on _____: _____   Time on_____: _____
        (social media network)   *(social media network)*

Time on _____: _____   Time on_____: _____
        (social media network)   *(social media network)*

How I felt in digital spaces this week

Things I posted this week

Positive content I saw (and my response)

Negative content I saw (and my response)

THINGS I LEARNED THIS WEEK

KIND THINGS I DID ONLINE

OTHER REFLECTIONS

AVERAGE TIME SPENT DAILY ON SOCIAL MEDIA THIS WEEK

Time on _____: _____   Time on_____: _____
          (social media network)   *(social media network)*

Time on _____: _____   Time on_____: _____
          (social media network)   *(social media network)*

How I felt in digital spaces this week

Things I posted this week

Positive content I saw (and my response)

Negative content I saw (and my response)

THINGS I LEARNED THIS WEEK

KIND THINGS I DID ONLINE

OTHER REFLECTIONS

AVERAGE TIME SPENT DAILY ON SOCIAL MEDIA THIS WEEK

Time on _____: _____   Time on_____: _____
     (social media network)   *(social media network)*

Time on _____: _____   Time on_____: _____
     (social media network)   *(social media network)*

HOW I FELT IN DIGITAL SPACES THIS WEEK

THINGS I POSTED THIS WEEK

POSITIVE CONTENT I SAW (AND MY RESPONSE)

NEGATIVE CONTENT I SAW (AND MY RESPONSE)

THINGS I LEARNED THIS WEEK

KIND THINGS I DID ONLINE

OTHER REFLECTIONS

AVERAGE TIME SPENT DAILY ON SOCIAL MEDIA THIS WEEK

Time on _____ : _____   Time on _____ : _____
        (social media network)   *(social media network)*

Time on _____ : _____   Time on _____ : _____
        (social media network)   *(social media network)*

WOW! Only 3 more months to go in your year of digital kindness!
What are you noticing about yourself and kindness in digital spaces?

HOW I FELT IN DIGITAL SPACES THIS WEEK

THINGS I POSTED THIS WEEK

POSITIVE CONTENT I SAW (AND MY RESPONSE)

NEGATIVE CONTENT I SAW (AND MY RESPONSE)

<u>THINGS I LEARNED THIS WEEK</u>

<u>KIND THINGS I DID ONLINE</u>

<u>OTHER REFLECTIONS</u>

<u>AVERAGE TIME SPENT DAILY ON SOCIAL MEDIA THIS WEEK</u>

Time on _____: _____   Time on_____: _____
        (social media network)   *(social media network)*

Time on _____: _____   Time on_____: _____
        (social media network)   *(social media network)*

How I felt in digital spaces this week

Things I posted this week

Positive content I saw (and my response)

Negative content I saw (and my response)

THINGS I LEARNED THIS WEEK

KIND THINGS I DID ONLINE

OTHER REFLECTIONS

AVERAGE TIME SPENT DAILY ON SOCIAL MEDIA THIS WEEK

Time on _____: _____   Time on_____: _____
      (social media network)   *(social media network)*

Time on _____: _____   Time on_____: _____
      (social media network)   *(social media network)*

How I felt in digital spaces this week

Things I posted this week

Positive content I saw (and my response)

Negative content I saw (and my response)

WEEK 38

THINGS I LEARNED THIS WEEK

KIND THINGS I DID ONLINE

OTHER REFLECTIONS

AVERAGE TIME SPENT DAILY ON SOCIAL MEDIA THIS WEEK

Time on _____: _____   Time on_____: _____
  (social media network)   *(social media network)*

Time on _____: _____   Time on_____: _____
  (social media network)   *(social media network)*

How I felt in digital spaces this week

Things I posted this week

Positive content I saw (and my response)

Negative content I saw (and my response)

WEEK 39

THINGS I LEARNED THIS WEEK

KIND THINGS I DID ONLINE

OTHER REFLECTIONS

AVERAGE TIME SPENT DAILY ON SOCIAL MEDIA THIS WEEK

Time on _____: _____   Time on_____: _____
(social media network)   *(social media network)*

Time on _____: _____   Time on_____: _____
(social media network)   *(social media network)*

HOW I FELT IN DIGITAL SPACES THIS WEEK

THINGS I POSTED THIS WEEK

POSITIVE CONTENT I SAW (AND MY RESPONSE)

NEGATIVE CONTENT I SAW (AND MY RESPONSE)

THINGS I LEARNED THIS WEEK

KIND THINGS I DID ONLINE

OTHER REFLECTIONS

AVERAGE TIME SPENT DAILY ON SOCIAL MEDIA THIS WEEK

Time on _____: _____   Time on_____: ___ __
(social media network)   _(social media network)_

Time on _____: _____   Time on_____: _____
(social media network)   _(social media network)_

How I felt in digital spaces this week

Things I posted this week

Positive content I saw (and my response)

Negative content I saw (and my response)

WEEK 40

THINGS I LEARNED THIS WEEK

KIND THINGS I DID ONLINE

OTHER REFLECTIONS

AVERAGE TIME SPENT DAILY ON SOCIAL MEDIA THIS WEEK

Time on _____ : _____   Time on_____ : _____
        (social media network)   *(social media network)*

Time on _____ : _____   Time on_____ : _____
        (social media network)   *(social media network)*

How I felt in digital spaces this week

Things I posted this week

Positive content I saw (and my response)

Negative content I saw (and my response)

WEEK 41

THINGS I LEARNED THIS WEEK

KIND THINGS I DID ONLINE

OTHER REFLECTIONS

AVERAGE TIME SPENT DAILY ON SOCIAL MEDIA THIS WEEK

Time on _____: _____
(social media network)

Time on_____: _____
(social media network)

Time on _____: _____
(social media network)

Time on_____: _____
(social media network)

HOW I FELT IN DIGITAL SPACES THIS WEEK

THINGS I POSTED THIS WEEK

POSITIVE CONTENT I SAW (AND MY RESPONSE)

NEGATIVE CONTENT I SAW (AND MY RESPONSE)

THINGS I LEARNED THIS WEEK

KIND THINGS I DID ONLINE

OTHER REFLECTIONS

AVERAGE TIME SPENT DAILY ON SOCIAL MEDIA THIS WEEK

Time on _____: _____   Time on_____: _____
       (social media network)   *(social media network)*

Time on _____: _____   Time on_____: _____
       (social media network)   *(social media network)*

HOW I FELT IN DIGITAL SPACES THIS WEEK

THINGS I POSTED THIS WEEK

POSITIVE CONTENT I SAW (AND MY RESPONSE)

NEGATIVE CONTENT I SAW (AND MY RESPONSE)

THINGS I LEARNED THIS WEEK

KIND THINGS I DID ONLINE

OTHER REFLECTIONS

AVERAGE TIME SPENT DAILY ON SOCIAL MEDIA THIS WEEK

Time on _____: _____   Time on_____: _____
    (social media network)   *(social media network)*

Time on _____: _____   Time on_____: _____
    (social media network)   *(social media network)*

HOW I FELT IN DIGITAL SPACES THIS WEEK

THINGS I POSTED THIS WEEK

POSITIVE CONTENT I SAW (AND MY RESPONSE)

NEGATIVE CONTENT I SAW (AND MY RESPONSE)

WEEK 44

THINGS I LEARNED THIS WEEK

KIND THINGS I DID ONLINE

OTHER REFLECTIONS

AVERAGE TIME SPENT DAILY ON SOCIAL MEDIA THIS WEEK

Time on _____: _____   Time on_____: _____
      (social media network)   *(social media network)*

Time on _____: _____   Time on_____: _____
      (social media network)   *(social media network)*

HOW I FELT IN DIGITAL SPACES THIS WEEK

THINGS I POSTED THIS WEEK

POSITIVE CONTENT I SAW (AND MY RESPONSE)

NEGATIVE CONTENT I SAW (AND MY RESPONSE)

THINGS I LEARNED THIS WEEK

KIND THINGS I DID ONLINE

OTHER REFLECTIONS

AVERAGE TIME SPENT DAILY ON SOCIAL MEDIA THIS WEEK

Time on _____ : _____   Time on _____ : _____
(social media network)   *(social media network)*

Time on _____ : _____   Time on _____ : _____
(social media network)   *(social media network)*

HOW I FELT IN DIGITAL SPACES THIS WEEK

THINGS I POSTED THIS WEEK

POSITIVE CONTENT I SAW (AND MY RESPONSE)

NEGATIVE CONTENT I SAW (AND MY RESPONSE)

THINGS I LEARNED THIS WEEK

KIND THINGS I DID ONLINE

OTHER REFLECTIONS

AVERAGE TIME SPENT DAILY ON SOCIAL MEDIA THIS WEEK

Time on _____: _____   Time on_____: _____
        (social media network)   *(social media network)*

Time on _____: _____   Time on_____: _____
        (social media network)   *(social media network)*

HOW I FELT IN DIGITAL SPACES THIS WEEK

THINGS I POSTED THIS WEEK

POSITIVE CONTENT I SAW (AND MY RESPONSE)

NEGATIVE CONTENT I SAW (AND MY RESPONSE)

WEEK 47

THINGS I LEARNED THIS WEEK

KIND THINGS I DID ONLINE

OTHER REFLECTIONS

AVERAGE TIME SPENT DAILY ON SOCIAL MEDIA THIS WEEK

Time on _____: _____ Time on_____: _____
(social media network)   *(social media network)*

Time on _____: _____ Time on_____: _____
(social media network)   *(social media network)*

How I felt in digital spaces this week

Things I posted this week

Positive content I saw (and my response)

Negative content I saw (and my response)

WEEK 48

<u>THINGS I LEARNED THIS WEEK</u>

<u>KIND THINGS I DID ONLINE</u>

<u>OTHER REFLECTIONS</u>

<u>AVERAGE TIME SPENT DAILY ON SOCIAL MEDIA THIS WEEK</u>

Time on _____: _____
(social media network)

Time on_____: _____
(social media network)

Time on _____: _____
(social media network)

Time on_____: _____
(social media network)

Congratulations! You've practiced digital kindness for an entire year!

How has your relationship with social media changed?

What uplifting habits have you developed?

What else do you want to reflect on at the end of this journey?

A closing invitation …

Thank you for choosing this journal to guide you in practicing digital kindness. I hope its pages have helped you develop caring social media attitudes and habits that bring you joy and peace in digital spaces. I'd love to hear about your experiences using this journal so I can continue to improve it. Please connect with me in any digital space you find me and share your thoughts. Together we can reclaim digital spaces and human places.

-Lauren

Lauren Hug

navigating our digital world
together

Lauren is passionate about helping people harness the power of digital media to share the world they want to see. Her positive, collaborative approach — as a speaker, writer, and conversation facilitator — has been described as empowering, life-changing, and even therapeutic.

She is the founder of HugSpeak Consulting, a participatory communication firm that develops strategies and workshops to plant and nurture vibrant communities in both digital and physical spaces. She is an attorney and certified mediator whose academic credentials include an LL.M. with merit from University College London, a J.D. with honors from the University of Texas School of Law, and a Bachelor of Journalism and Bachelor of Arts in Spanish from the University of Texas.

OTHER BOOKS BY LAUREN

Digital Kindness: Being Human in a Hyper-Connected World

Digital Grace: Pouring Benevolence into an Outraged World

The Professional Woman's Guide to Getting Promoted

The Manager's Guide to Presentations

LAUREN'S SUBSTACK NEWSLETTER

Digital Hope

Printed in Great Britain
by Amazon

33134567R00165